OXFORD

8 Maths Links

Ray Allan

Martin Williams

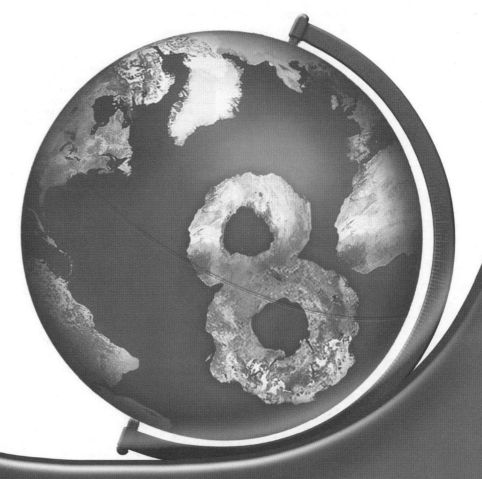

Practice Book

OXFORD
UNIVERSITY PRESS

Great Clarendon Street, Oxford OX2 6DP

Oxford University Press is a department of the University of Oxford.
It furthers the University's objective of excellence in research, scholarship, and
education by publishing worldwide in

Oxford New York

Auckland Cape Town Dar es Salaam Hong Kong Karachi
Kuala Lumpur Madrid Melbourne Mexico City Nairobi
New Delhi Shanghai Taipei Toronto

With offices in

Argentina Austria Brazil Chile Czech Republic France Greece
Guatemala Hungary Italy Japan Poland Portugal Singapore
South Korea Switzerland Thailand Turkey Ukraine Vietnam

British Library Cataloguing in Publication Data

Data available

ISBN: 9780-19-915294-0

10 9 8 7

Printed in Great Britain by Ashford Ltd, Gosport

Acknowledgments
The Press would like to thank Pete Crawford for his invaluable contribution to
Case Studies.

Paper used in the production of this book is a natural, recyclable product made
from wood grown in sustainable forests. The manufacturing process conforms
to the environmental regulations to the country of origin.

1 Use each number line to complete the problem.

a -4 + 7 = _____

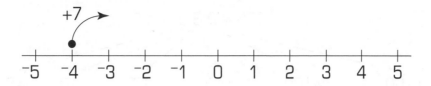

b 3 − 6 = _____

c -5 + 3 = _____

d -2 − 7 = _____

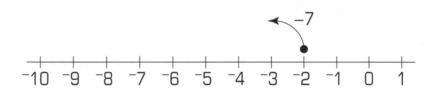

2 Complete these problems. Use the number line to help you.

Negative numbers move to the **left**

Positive numbers move to the **right**

a -9 − 6 = _____ b 4 − 6 = _____

c -6 + 2 = _____ d -5 − 13 = _____

e -2 + 7 = _____ f 7 − 11 = _____

g -3 + 10 = _____ h -3 − 5 = _____

i -4 − 4 = _____ j -6 + 6 = _____

k 2 − 9 = _____ l -5 + 12 = _____

1 **a** Fill in the boxes to show how to work out 120 + 235.

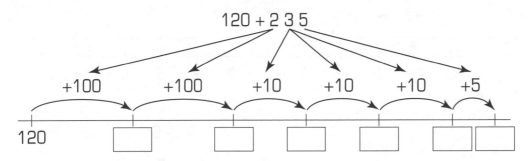

b Show another way to add the numbers. Show all of the stages.

Try to use a jotting that is quicker.

120

2 **a** Use this number line to work out 567 − 149.

Count on from 149 to 562.

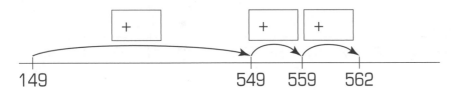

b Add the differences together to complete the subtraction:

567 − 149 = _____

3 Use 'taking away' jottings on this number line to work out 725 − 238.

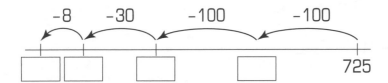

1

> ► A number in the 2 times table is a **multiple** of 2.
>
>   2, 4, 6, 8, 10, 12, 14, ...
>
> ► The multiples of 3 are in the 3 times table.
>
>   3, 6, 9, 12, 15, ...

Use these multiples to complete these factor trees:

a

b

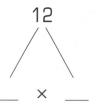

c

2 This box is full of numbers.

Write the numbers from the box that divide exactly by:

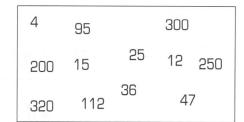

a   2 _____

b   5 _____

c   10 _____

d   100 _____

1 Here are the names of the some units.

Find the units and highlight them in the word search.

MILLIMETRE
CENTIMETRE
METRE
KILOMETRE
GRAM
KILOGRAM
MILLILITRE
LITRE

L	O	K	B	A	K	N	C	T	P	O
G	M	I	L	L	I	M	E	T	R	E
R	I	L	V	S	L	J	P	K	R	S
A	L	O	M	D	O	V	T	C	H	B
M	L	G	E	H	M	L	I	T	R	E
A	I	R	N	D	E	Y	L	E	G	O
K	L	A	D	N	T	W	I	C	J	U
N	I	M	E	T	R	E	S	X	T	H
W	T	P	O	N	E	F	R	D	P	R
F	R	L	B	K	U	N	T	S	G	V
C	E	N	T	I	M	E	T	R	E	K

2 Rewrite each sentence using the correct units.

The first one is done for you.

a He is 168 **litres** tall.

He is 168 centimetres tall.

b The tiny bird only weighed 27 **millimetres**.

_____

c The barrel held 40 **metres** of water.

_____

d The distance from Ballin to Galway is 50 **grams**.

_____

> Choose your answers from this list:
>
> grams
>
> centimetres
>
> kilometres
>
> litres

3 Circle the answer to make each statement true.

a A millimetre is **more than** / **less than** a metre.

b A kilogram is **more than** / **less than** a gram.

c A kilometre is **more than** / **less than** a metre.

d A millilitre is **more than** / **less than** a litre.

2d Perimeter and area

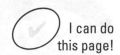

► The perimeter of a shape is the distance around the edge.

► The area of a shape is the amount of surface it covers.

Each of these squares represents 1 cm × 1 cm.

Find the perimeter and area of each shape.

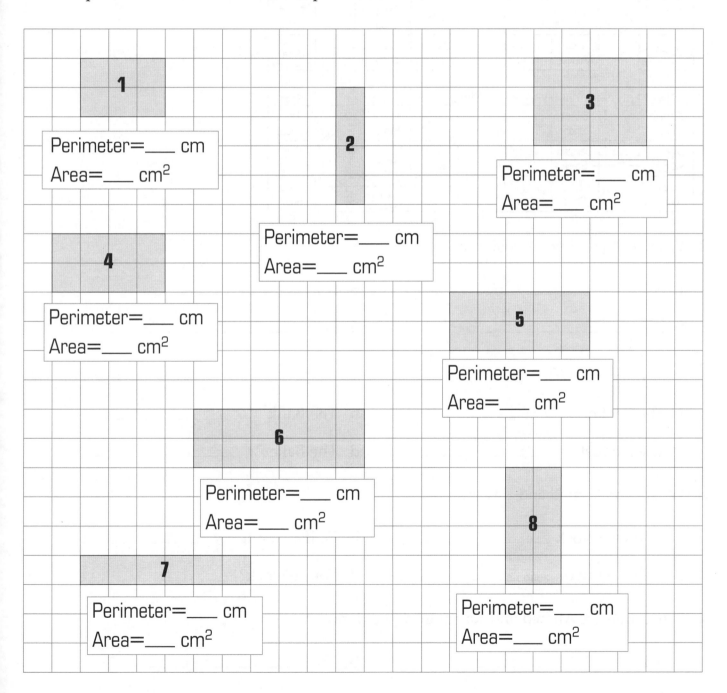

1

Perimeter=___ cm
Area=___ cm²

2

Perimeter=___ cm
Area=___ cm²

3

Perimeter=___ cm
Area=___ cm²

4

Perimeter=___ cm
Area=___ cm²

5

Perimeter=___ cm
Area=___ cm²

6

Perimeter=___ cm
Area=___ cm²

7

Perimeter=___ cm
Area=___ cm²

8

Perimeter=___ cm
Area=___ cm²

I can do this page!

Ahmed and Kay are shopping.

Here is a grid plan of the route they take.

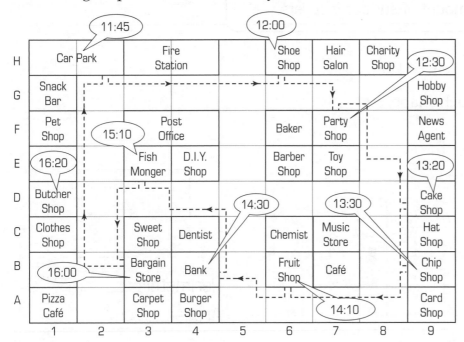

1 What will you find at position:

   a 6C _____

   b 6H _____

   c 1G _____

   d 9G? _____

2 Give positions for:

   a The Pet Shop _____

   b The Bank _____

   c The Dentist _____

   d The Baker? _____

3 Where are Ahmed and Kay at:

   a Twelve o'clock _____

   b Half past one _____

   c Half past two _____

   d Four o'clock? _____

4 What time are Ahmed and Kay at grid position:

   a 6H _____

   b 1H _____

   c 1D _____

   d 3E? _____

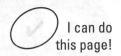

1 Draw arrows from these statements to a point on the scale to show how likely you think they are.

> The chance of winning a lottery without a ticket.

> The chance of flipping a tail on a normal coin.

> The chance of picking a red card from a bag of 4 red cards.

> The chance of rolling a 6 on a dice.

Impossible ——————————— Even chance ——————————— Certain

> The chance of choosing a boy's name from a bag containing 10 girls' names and 1 boy's name.

> The chance of rolling an odd number on a dice.

> The chance of picking a black card from a bag with 4 black cards and 1 red card.

2 Describe an event with each of these probabilities:

Even chance _____

_____

High probability _____

_____

Impossible _____

_____

Low probability _____

_____

Certain _____

_____

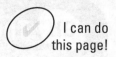

1 The probability of a spinner landing on red is $\frac{1}{2}$.

Colour each spinner to show this probability.

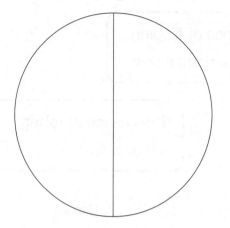 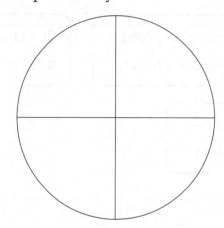 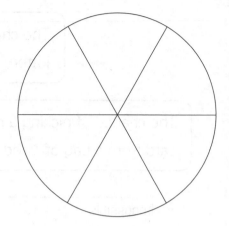

2 The probability of a spinner landing on green is $\frac{2}{3}$.

Colour each spinner to show this probability.

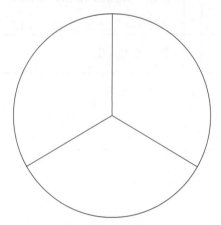 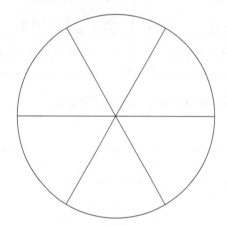 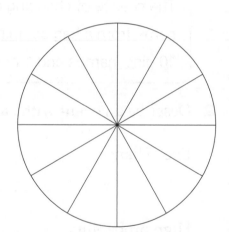

3 The probability of a spinner landing on blue is $\frac{3}{4}$.

Colour each spinner to show this probability.

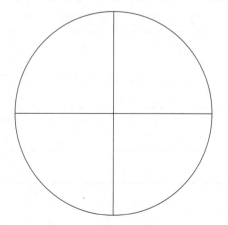 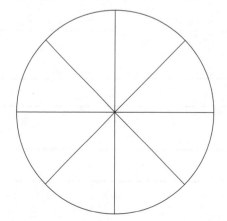 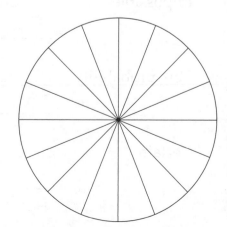

8

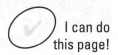

Mike thinks that:

People with brown hair
tend to have brown eyes.

People with blond hair
tend to have blue eyes.

1 Survey all the people in your class that have brown hair or blond hair.

Write your results in these tables:

	Colour of eyes				
	blue	brown	hazel	grey	green
Students with brown hair					

	Colour of eyes				
	blue	brown	hazel	grey	green
Students with blond hair					

2 Do your results support Mike's hypothesis that:

'People with brown hair tend to have brown eyes'?

Explain your answer.

_____

_____

3 Do your results support Mike's hypothesis that:

'People with blond hair tend to have blue eyes'?

Explain your answer.

_____

_____

4 Which eye colour is the most common overall? _____

5 Which eye colour is the least common overall? _____

1 If I choose card **5**

I have to pay ....

I have a ..... in ...... chance of winning.

I have a ..... in ...... chance of losing.

2 If I choose card **2**

I have to pay ....

I have a ..... in ...... chance of winning.

I have a ..... in ...... chance of losing.

SPIN TO WIN!

The spinner will spin when all 5 numbers have been bought.

The person with the number the spinner stops at wins a fabulous prize!

a prize every game!

50p per go!

3 If I choose cards **1** and **3**

I have to pay ....

I have a ..... in ...... chance of winning.

I have a ..... in ...... chance of losing.

If the stallholder gave money as a prize, how much do you think it should be?

4 To be certain of winning, I would have to choose cards

....

I would have to pay ....

1 Number all the decimal markers on this line.

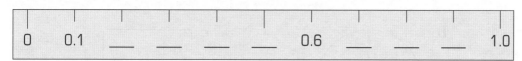

2 Write the missing decimal numbers in the empty boxes on these number lines.

a

1.8 ☐ 2.0 ☐

b

☐ 8.3 ☐ 8.5

c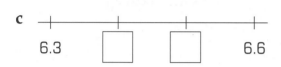

6.3 ☐ ☐ 6.6

d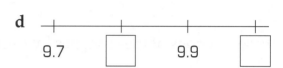

9.7 ☐ 9.9 ☐

3 Calculate the numbers that are 0.9 more than 2.4 and 0.9 less than 2.4.

Use this number line to help you.

2.4

▶ 0.9 more than 2.4 is _____

▶ 0.9 less than 2.4 is _____

4 Estimate the positions of these numbers on this number line.

Use arrows to point to your estimates.

a 5.8   **b** 3.1

c 4.5   **d** 5.2

3.0   4.0   5.0   6.0

4b Fractions

1 Shade these fractions of these shapes.

a

One half $\left(\frac{1}{2}\right)$

b

One third $\left(\frac{1}{3}\right)$

c

One sixth $\left(\frac{1}{6}\right)$

2 Shade these fractions of these shapes by estimating.

a $\frac{1}{2}$

b $\frac{1}{3}$

c $\frac{1}{4}$

3 Colour $\frac{1}{3}$ of each set of tokens.

a

b

c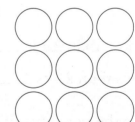

4 Colour $\frac{1}{4}$ of each set of tiles.

a

b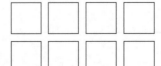

c

1 Complete these diagrams to help you to simplify these fractions.

a

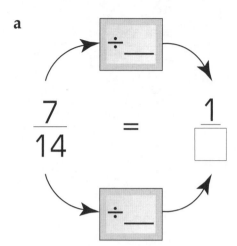

$$\frac{7}{14} = \frac{1}{\Box}$$

÷ ___

÷ ___

b

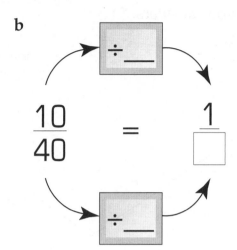

$$\frac{10}{40} = \frac{1}{\Box}$$

÷ ___

÷ ___

2 Complete the fractions in the circles so that they are all equivalent to $\frac{1}{4}$.

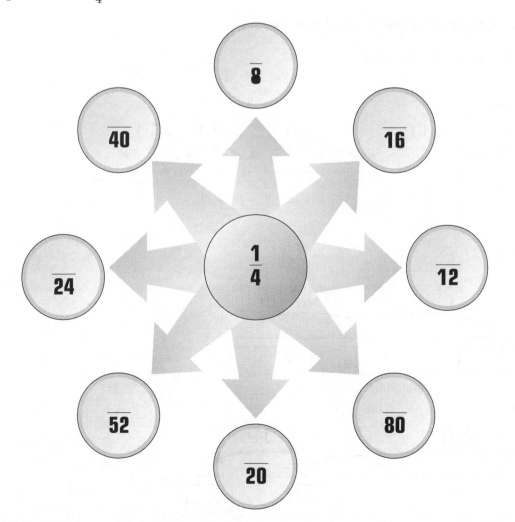

$\frac{}{8}$

$\frac{}{40}$

$\frac{}{16}$

$\frac{}{24}$

$\frac{1}{4}$

$\frac{}{12}$

$\frac{}{52}$

$\frac{}{80}$

$\frac{}{20}$

1 Measure the sides of this quadrilateral. You will need to use decimals in your answers.

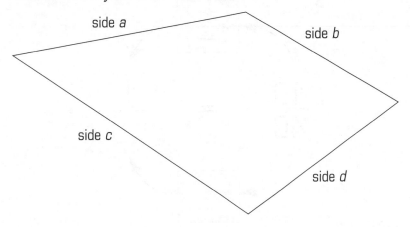

side *a*

side *b*

side *c*

side *d*

Side *a* is _____ cm   Side *b* is _____ cm

Side *c* is _____ cm   Side *d* is _____ cm

2 Use these number lines to add the pairs of numbers.

Fill in the spaces in the boxes to help.

a 5.7 + 3.2 = _____

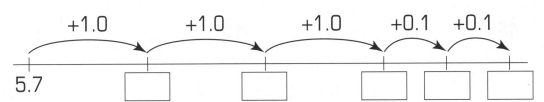

+1.0   +1.0   +1.0   +0.1 +0.1

5.7

b 9.6 + 2.7 = _____

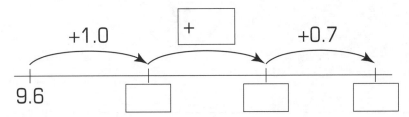

+1.0   +   +0.7

9.6

c 12.8 + 5.9 = _____

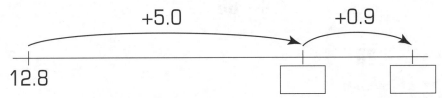

+5.0   +0.9

12.8

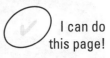
I can do
this page!

1 Shade $\frac{1}{4}$ of this strip.

2 a Divide these circles into quarters $\left(\frac{1}{4}\right)$ on this grid.

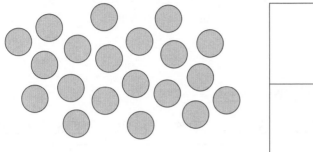

Use the drawing to find:

b $\frac{1}{4}$ of 20   Answer: _____

c $\frac{1}{2}$ of 20.   Answer: _____

3 a Divide these circles into thirds $\left(\frac{1}{3}\right)$ on this grid.

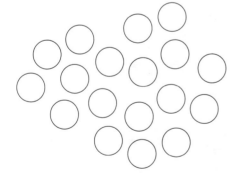

Use the drawing to find:

b $\frac{1}{3}$ of 18   Answer: _____

c $\frac{2}{3}$ of 18.   Answer: _____

I can do this page!

1 Use this scale to find these percentages of £500.

| 0% | 10% | 20% | 30% | 40% | 50% | 60% | 70% | 80% | 90% | 100% |
| £0 | £50 | £100 | £150 | £200 | £250 | £300 | £350 | £400 | £450 | £500 |

a 10% of £500 = _____

b 70% of £500 = _____

c 90% of £500 = _____

2 Complete this scale to show £30 in 10 percent intervals.

| 0% | 10% | 20% | 30% | 40% | 50% | 60% | 70% | 80% | 90% | 100% |
| £0 | | | | | | | | | | £30 |

3 Complete these function machines to show how to find:

a 10% of an amount

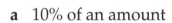

b 40% of an amount

c 90% of an amount

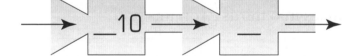

d 30% of an amount

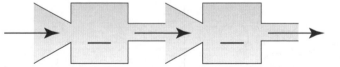

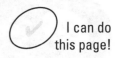
1 Colour this 100 grid:

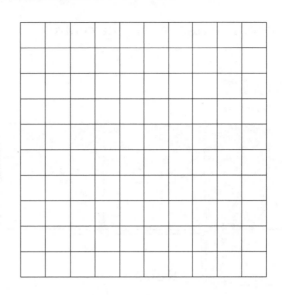

a 10% blue

b 20% red

c 43% green

d 7% orange

e What percentage is left uncoloured?

_____%

2 Use arrows to link the fractions and percentages that are equivalent.

12%   100% $\frac{60}{100}$ $\frac{1}{10}$ $\frac{23}{100}$ $\frac{1}{4}$ 17%   50%   90%

$\frac{100}{100}$ $\frac{12}{100}$ 25%   60% $\frac{9}{10}$ $\frac{17}{100}$ 10%   23% $\frac{50}{100}$

3 Complete this table.

Use the 100 grid in question 1 to help you.

Fraction			$\frac{3}{10}$		$\frac{69}{100}$	$\frac{3}{4}$		1
Percentage	1%	10%		50%			80%	

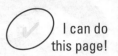

Play this game. The rules are in the centre.

Hint for $5d - 2$:

$\times$ 5 first, then $- 2$

START

FINISH

d	d + 3	5d – 2	8 – d	3d

d + 1 – d	d + 1
4d – 1	2d + 1
3d – 3	2d
10 – d	d + 4
2 + d	2d – 3

3d	d – 1	3d + 3	5d	10 + d

Rules

▶ Each player needs a dice and a counter.

▶ Take turns to roll the dice.

▶ Use the number on the dice as the value of *d* for the square your counter is on.

▶ Work out the value of the expression.

▶ Move forward that number of squares. If the answer is negative you move backwards.

▶ You win if you complete 3 laps of the track first, landing on or past the finish square.

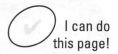

▶ The perimeter of a shape is the distance around
the edge.

1 Find the lengths of the sides of these squares.

a

Perimeter =
8 cm

Length = _____ cm

b

Perimeter =
20 cm

Length = _____ cm

c

Perimeter =
16 cm

Length = _____ cm

2 The perimeter of this square is 8*t* cm.

Each side is 2*t* cm long.

Perimeter = 2*t* + 2*t* + 2*t* + 2*t* cm

   = 4 × 2*t* cm

   = 8*t* cm.

2*t* cm

2*t* cm   2*t* cm

2*t* cm

The squares are not
drawn accurately.
Do not try to
measure them.

Find the length of the sides of these squares.

a Perimeter = 8*m* cm

Length = _____ cm

b Perimeter = 20*y* cm

Length = _____ cm

c Perimeter = 16*p* cm

Length = _____ cm

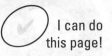

1 This is an equilateral triangle.

The length of each side is d cm.

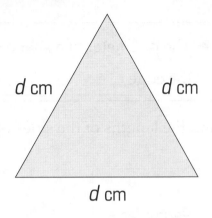

d cm   *d* cm

d cm

a Find the perimeter of the triangle using d for
the length of each side.

Perimeter = _____ + _____ + _____ cm

= _____ cm

b Find the perimeter of the triangle when the value of d is:

i 5 cm   **ii** 7 cm   **iii** 15 cm

Show your calculations here:

i Perimeter = _____ × _____ cm   **ii** Perimeter = _____ × _____ cm

= _____ cm   = _____ cm

iii Perimeter = _____ × _____ cm

= _____ cm

2 The area of this rectangle = length×width

= a cm × b cm.

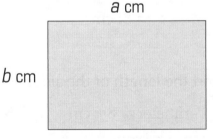

a cm

b cm   *b* cm

a cm

Substitute these values for a and b to calculate
the area when:

a $a = 5$ cm and $b = 3$ cm.

Area = $a \times b$

= _____ cm × _____ cm

= _____ cm^2

b $a = 4$ cm and $b = 2$ cm.

Area = $a \times b$

= _____ cm × _____ cm

= _____ cm^2

c $a = 10$ cm and $b = 7$ cm.

Area = $a \times b$

= _____ cm × _____ cm

= _____ cm^2

cm^2 is a unit of area.

6a Angles

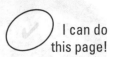
Name and write a description for each of these angles.

Choose your answers from these lists:

Angle name	Angle description
Straight line	Exactly 180°
Right angle	More than 90° and less than 180°
Acute angle	More than 0° and less than 90°
Obtuse angle	Exactly 90°

Angle	Angle name	Angle description
1 	_____	_____ _____
2	_____	_____ _____
3	_____	_____ _____
4 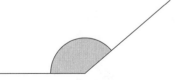	_____	_____ _____

1 Angles on a straight line

Calculate and write in the missing angles.

> There are 180° on a straight line.

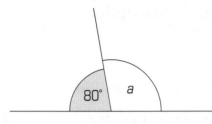

$a =$ _____ °

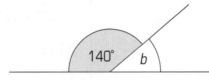

$b =$ _____ °

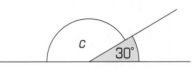

$c =$ _____ °

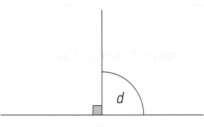

$d =$ _____ °

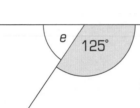

$e =$ _____ °

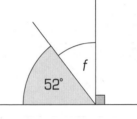

$f =$ _____ °

2 Angles around a point

Calculate and write in the missing angles.

> There are 360° in a full turn.

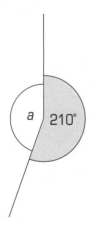

$a =$ _____ °

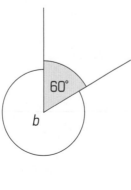

$b =$ _____ °

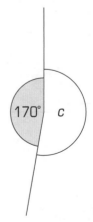

$c =$ _____ °

▶ The 3 angles in a triangle always add up to 180°.

$60° + 40° + 80° = 180°$

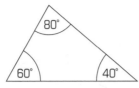

a Find the missing angles in these triangles.

b Name each triangle.

Choose from this list: | Scalene | Right-angled | Isosceles | Equilateral

1

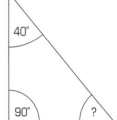

? = _____ °

Name: _____

2

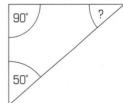

? = _____ °

Name: _____

3

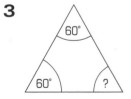

? = _____ °

Name: _____

4

? = _____ °

Name: _____

5

70° 70°

?

? = _____ °

Name: _____

6

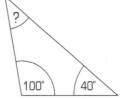

? = _____ °

Name: _____

There are lots of 3-D shapes in this picture.

Colour the 3-D shapes:

▶ **Cubes** and **cuboids** – green

▶ **Cylinders** – red

▶ **Cones** – blue

▶ **Pyramids** – brown

▶ **Triangular prisms** – purple

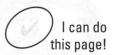

1 Write on the missing weights to make the scales balance.

a
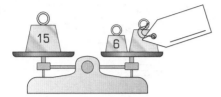

b

c

d

2 Write on weights to make the scales unbalanced.

a
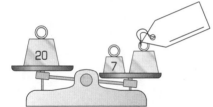

b

c

d

e
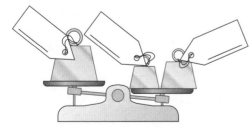

f

1 Write the inverse operation into the boxes.

a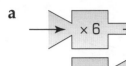

b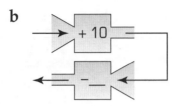

c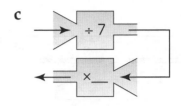

d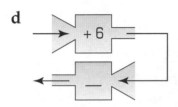

e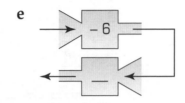

f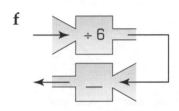

2 Use inverses to find the value of the **input symbol**.

The first one is done for you

a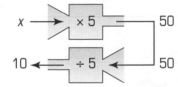

b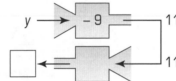

c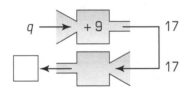

d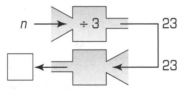

3 This equation has been written as a function machine:

$x - 13 = 20$

Use the inverse to find the value of x.

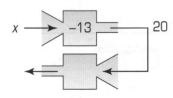

$x = $ _____

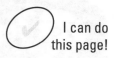

1 This function multiplies the input number by 3:

input ⟶ ×3 ⟶ output

Use the function to complete this table.

input	0	1	2	3	4	5	6	7	8
output	0	3	6						

2 Write the inputs and outputs as graph coordinates.

(0, 0)

(1, ___)

(2, ___)

(3, ___)

(4, ___)

(5, ___)

(6, ___)

(7, ___)

(8, ___)

3 Plot these coordinates into this grid.

4 Draw a line through the coordinates.

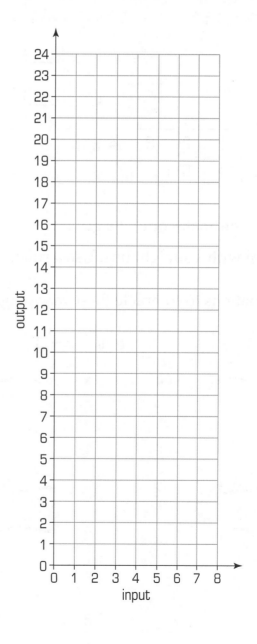

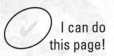

1 Here is an equation: $y = x - 2$

   a Use the equation to complete the mapping and the table.

     Write the mapping pairs as coordinates.

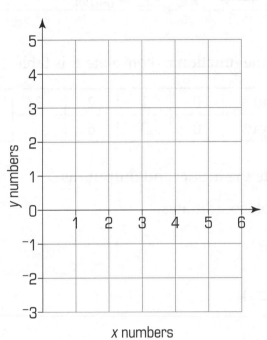

x numbers → **y numbers**

0		−2	(____ , ____)
1		−1	(____ , ____)
2		0	(____ , ____)
3		___	(____ , ____)
5		___	(____ , ____)

x	0	1	2	3	4	5
y	−2	−1	0			

   b Plot the coordinates onto the grid.

     Join them with a straight line. Use a ruler.

2 Use the equations to complete these mappings:

   a $y = x - 3$ **b** $y = x + 3$ **c** $y = x \times 3$

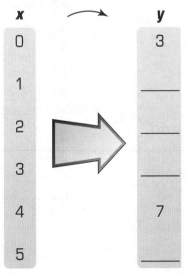
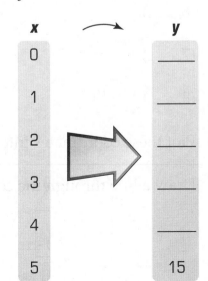

a

x		y
0		−3
1		−2
2		−1
3		___
4		___
5		___

b

x		y
0		3
1		___
2		___
3		___
4		7
5		___

c

x		y
0		___
1		___
2		___
3		___
4		___
5		15

8a Rounding

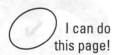

1 Write the **rounded** position of the arrow in the empty box.

Round to the nearest whole number.

If a digit is 5 or above, round up.

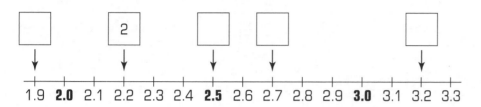

| | 2 | | | | |

1.9 **2.0** 2.1 2.2 2.3 2.4 **2.5** 2.6 2.7 2.8 2.9 **3.0** 3.1 3.2 3.3

2 a Write a number in each box that would round to the nearest 10.

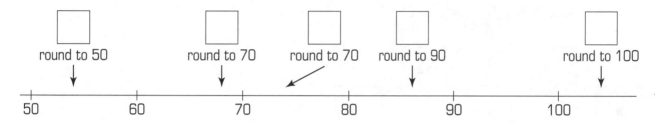

round to 50   round to 70   round to 70   round to 90   round to 100

50   60   70   80   90   100

b Write a number in each box that would round to the nearest 100.

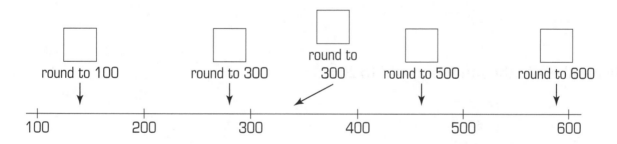

round to 100   round to 300   round to 300   round to 500   round to 600

100   200   300   400   500   600

3 Measure this line and write its length to the nearest centimetre.

_____

Write your answer in the box.

The line is ☐ cm rounded to the nearest centimetre.

1 The diagram shows pairs of numbers that add to 20.

Write numbers in the squares to complete the diagram.

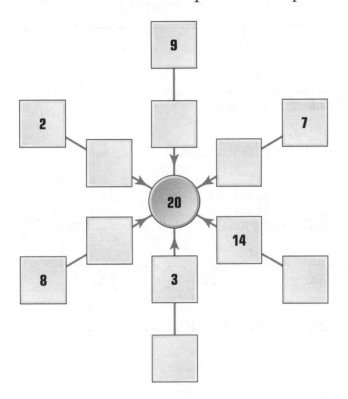

2 Write numbers in the squares to add to 200.

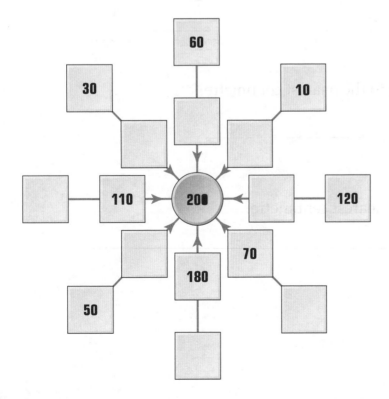

8d Subtracting decimals

1 Use this number line to work out the differences between each pair of numbers.

a 0.3 and 0.9 _____

b 0.6 and 1.0 _____

c 0.7 and 1.1 _____

d 0.8 and 1.5 _____

e 2.2 and 3.0 _____

f 1.9 and 2.7 _____

g 0.7 and 2.8 _____

h 0.9 and 2.9 _____

2 Use these number lines to work out the difference between 6.3 and 10.7. Try both these methods.

a Count on from 6.3 to 10.7.

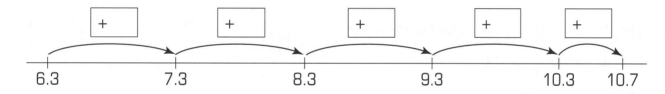

$10.7 - 6.3 =$ _____

b Subtract back from 10.7 to 6.3.

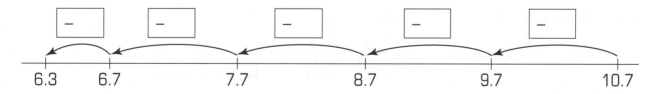

$10.7 - 6.3 =$ _____

8e Dividing with decimals

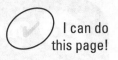

I can do this page!

1 Divide these numbers by 10.

Move each digit 1 place to the right.

a 69 ÷ 10 = _____

H	T	U	.	$\frac{1}{10}$
6	9	.	0	÷ 10

☐ . ☐

b 125 ÷ 10 = _____

H	T	U	.	$\frac{1}{10}$
1	2	5	.	0	÷ 10

☐ ☐ . ☐

c 26 ÷ 10 = _____

H	T	U	.	$\frac{1}{10}$
2	6	.	0	÷ 10

☐ . ☐

d 4 ÷ 10 = _____

H	T	U	.	$\frac{1}{10}$
		4	.	0	÷ 10

☐ . ☐

2 This line is split into 10 equal parts or $\frac{1}{10}$s.

1 ÷ 10 means $\frac{1}{10}$ or 0.1.

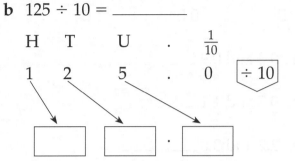

a 1 ÷ 5 means $\frac{1}{5}$.

Write 1 ÷ 5 as a decimal.

_____

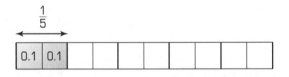

b 2 ÷ 5 means $\frac{2}{5}$.

Write 2 ÷ 5 as a decimal.

_____

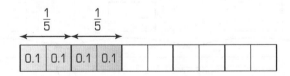

c Write 3 ÷ 5 as a decimal.

_____

d 1 ÷ 4 means $\frac{1}{4}$.

Write 1 ÷ 4 as a decimal.

_____

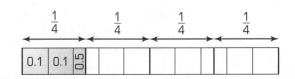

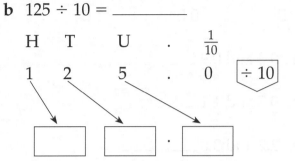

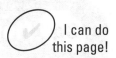

1 Complete these grids to multiply the numbers.

a 13×7

×	10	3
7	70	

$13 \times 7 = 70 +$ _____

$= $ _____

b 24×8

×	20	4
8		32

$24 \times 8 =$ _____ $+ 32$

$= $ _____

2 Find approximations for these multiplications.

> The sign ≈ means 'is approximately equal to'.

a 8.2×5

$\approx 8 \times 5 =$ _____

b 5.9×6

$\approx$ _____ $\times 6 =$ _____

c 9.1×4

$\approx$ _____ $\times$ _____ $=$ _____

d 3.7×8

$\approx$ _____ $\times$ _____ $=$ _____

3 Complete these grids to multiply the numbers.

Use your approximations in question 2 to help you.

a $8.2 \times 5 =$ _____

×	8●	2
5		

b $5.9 \times 6 =$ _____

×	50	9
6		

c $9.1 \times 4 =$ _____

×	90	1
4		

d $3.7 \times 8 =$ _____

×	30	7
8		

1 Divide the numbers on the left by 10.

Match them with arrows to the answers

on the right.

One is done for you.

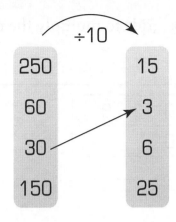

÷10

250	15
60	3
30	6
150	25

2 Fill in the boxes to complete these divisions.

a 352 ÷ 16

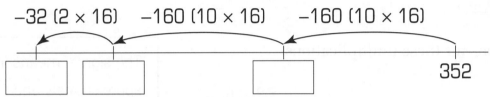

−32 (2 × 16)   −160 (10 × 16)   −160 (10 × 16)

352

b How many 16s are there in 352?

Answer: _____

3 a Complete these subtractions to work out 470 ÷ 18.

470

− 180   → 10 × 18

☐

− 180   → 10 × 18

☐

− 90   → 5 × 18

☐

− 18   → 1 × 18

☐

b How many 18s are there in 470? Answer: _____

c What is the remainder? Answer: _____

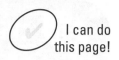
1 **a** Draw the reflection of triangle ABC in the mirror line.

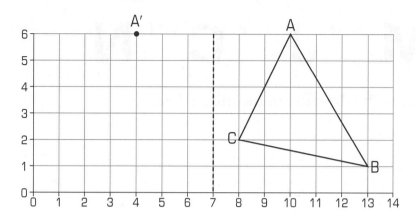

b Give the coordinates of the reflected shape.

A′ = (_____, _____)   B′ = (_____, _____)   C′ = (_____, _____)

2 This mirror line runs across the grid diagonally.

a Mark the reflection of each point on the grid.

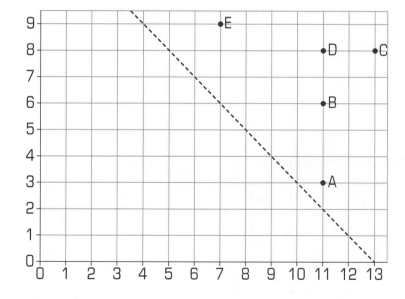

b Give the coordinates of the reflected points.

A′ = (_____, _____)   B′ = (_____, _____)   C′ = (_____, _____)

D′ = (_____, _____)   E′ = (_____, _____)

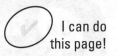

1 Draw all the lines of symmetry on each letter.

^a **H** ^b **R** ^c **M** ^d **J** ^e **C** ^f **N**

2 Complete the vampire by reflecting the drawing in the mirror line.

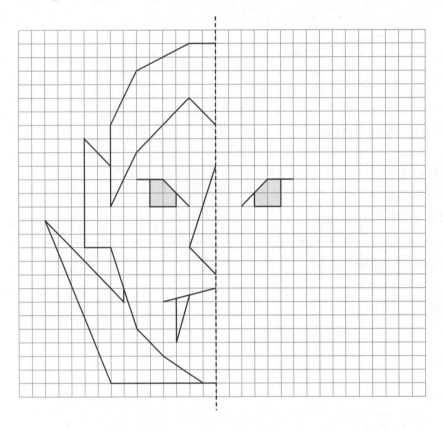

3 Draw the reflection of each shape in the mirror line.

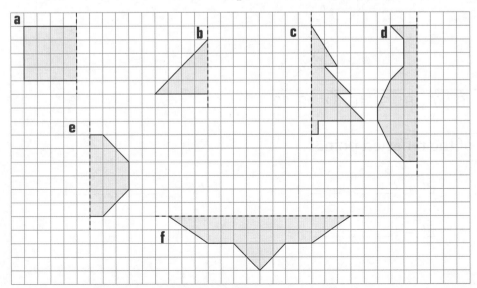

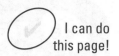

1 For each turn, write if it is:

▶ clockwise or anticlockwise

▶ 90° or 180°

a   b   c   d

▶ clockwise   ▶ _____   ▶ _____   ▶ _____

▶ _____°   ▶ _____°   ▶ _____°   ▶ _____°

2 **a** Rotate this shape **90° clockwise** about the X.

b Rotate this shape **90° anticlockwise** about the X.

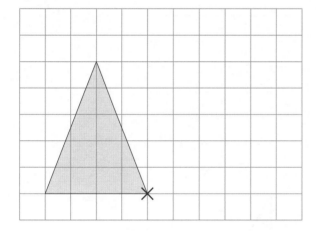

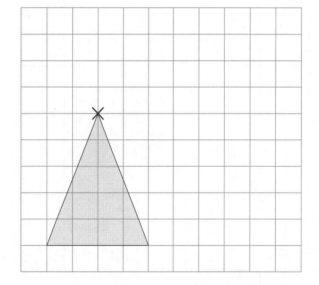

3 Rotate this shape **180° clockwise** about the X.

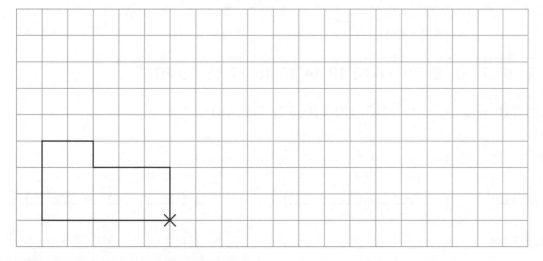

Use these instructions to translate each shape and draw its new

position on the grid.

Give the coordinates of each shape after translation.

The first one is done for you.

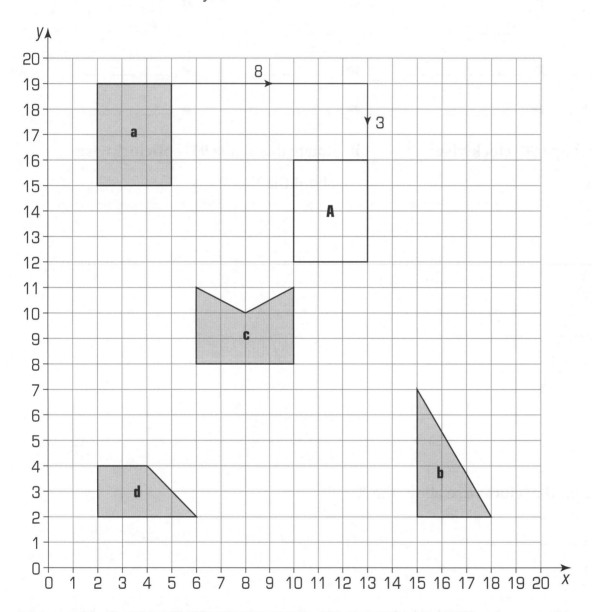

Shape **a**   8 right and 3 down   (13, 16) (13, 12) (10, 12) (10, 16)

Shape **b**   14 left and 7 up   (___, ___) (___, ___) (___, ___)

Shape **c**   9 right and 8 up   (___, ___) (___, ___) (___, ___) (___, ___) (___, ___)

Shape **d**   5 right and 3 up   (___, ___) (___, ___) (___, ___) (___, ___)

1 Follow these LOGO commands for each grid.

The cursor is always pointing up the page at the start.

a

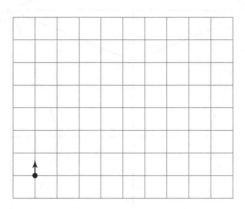

FORWARD 6

RIGHT 90

FORWARD 6

RIGHT 90

FORWARD 6

RIGHT 90

FORWARD 6

What shape have you drawn?

_____

b

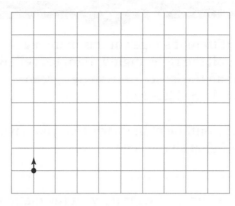

RIGHT 90

FORWARD 8

LEFT 90

FORWARD 4

LEFT 90

FORWARD 8

LEFT 90

FORWARD 4

What shape have you drawn?

_____

2 Write the LOGO commands for this drawing.

Start: Left 90

Forward _____

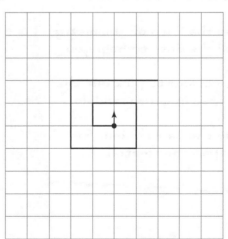

Mandalas

???

1 Look for different shapes in this mandala.
   a Colour all the right angled triangles yellow.
   b Colour all the isosceles triangles green.
   c Colour all the kites red.

2 Look at the outline of the parts that you have coloured. What shape is it?

   ....

3 Mark all the lines of symmetry on the mandala.

Draw your own symmetrical mandala in this circle.

Use the lines of symmetry and the dots to help you.

Use colour to pick out the shapes in your mandala.

Use the same colour for shapes that match.

10a Sequences

1 Use the rule and number line to write the next 5 numbers in each sequence.

a 2 , _____ , _____ , _____ , _____ , _____

> The first term is 2.
> The rule is +3.

b 22 , _____ , _____ , _____ , _____ , _____

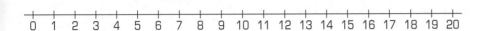

> The first term is 22.
> The rule is ⁻3.

c ⁻7 , _____ , _____ , _____ , _____ , _____

> The first term is ⁻7.
> The rule is +3.

2 Complete the next 3 terms in each sequence.

Write the first term and the rule for each sequence.

a 4, 7, 10, 13, _____ , _____ , _____

The first term is 4, the rule is add 3.

b 36, 31, 26, 21, _____ , _____ , _____

The first term is _____, the rule is _____.

c ⁻8, ⁻5, ⁻2, 1, _____ , _____ , _____

The first term is _____, the rule is _____.

d 14, 10, 6, 2, _____ , _____ , _____

The first term is _____, the rule is _____.

e ⁻20, ⁻16, ⁻12, ⁻8, _____ , _____ , _____

The first term is _____, the rule is _____.

Copyright OUP. Photocopying prohibited.

41

1 Geeta uses 'L' shaped blocks to lay a path.

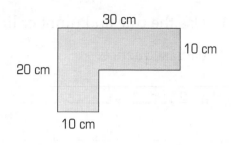

30 cm

10 cm

20 cm

10 cm

a She lays the first 4 blocks.

Continue her pattern to cover the space completely.

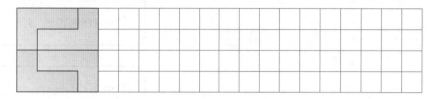

b How many blocks are used to lay the path? _____

c What is the width of the whole path? _____

d What is the length of the whole path? _____

2 Bolts are used to fasten a fence to some posts.

3 bolts are used on each post.

How many bolts are needed for

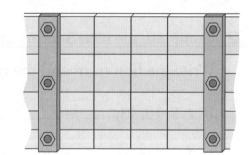

a 5 posts _____

b 11 posts _____

c 19 posts? _____

3 Each bolt needs 3 washers and 2 nuts.

Complete the table to show the link between the number

of bolts, washers and nuts.

Bolts	Washers	Nuts
4 ➡	12 ➡	8
2	___	___
___	___	12
___	15	___
10	___	___
___	27	___

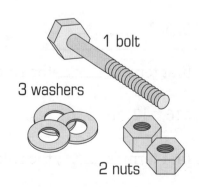

1 bolt

3 washers

2 nuts

1 Sort these data sources into the correct list:

survey	newspaper	library	database	website
magazine	questionnaire	experiment	interview	

Primary data

_____
_____
_____
_____
_____
_____
_____
_____

Secondary data

_____
_____
_____
_____
_____
_____
_____
_____

2 Which statement is the easiest hypothesis to test?

A hypothesis is what you say may happen.

A	Left-handed people are better tennis players.

B	Left-handed people win more games of tennis.

C	A left-handed person is more likely to beat a right-handed person at tennis.

Answer: _____

I would test this hypothesis by _____

_____

_____

Eight students in 8H want to see who has the best throw.

They decide to see who can throw a bean-bag the furthest.

1   Imagine you are doing this experiment.

Where would you hold this in your school?

_____

2   What equipment would you use to measure a throw?

_____

3   How many trials would each person have? _____

4   How would you decide who won? _____

_____

5   Design a data collection sheet to record the data.

Name	Sex:M/F	

6   Pete says: | The boys will be able to throw the bean-bag further than the girls. |

Describe how you would use your data to test this hypothesis.

_____

_____

_____

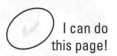

1 Roll a dice 30 times. Record your results on this frequency table.

Number	Tally	Frequency
⚅		
⚄		
⚃		
⚂		
⚁		
⚀		

2 Plot your results on this bar chart.

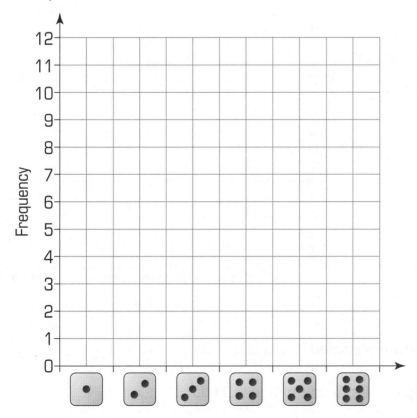

3 What was the most common score? _____

1 Jack collected data on how students in Year 8 travel to school.

Draw his data as a bar chart on the grid.

Means of travel	Tally	Frequency
Bus	ⵂⵂ ⵂⵂ ⵂⵂ III	18
Car	ⵂⵂ IIII	9
Cycle	ⵂⵂ ⵂⵂ II	12
Walk	ⵂⵂ ⵂⵂ ⵂⵂ ⵂⵂ II	22
Train	IIII	4

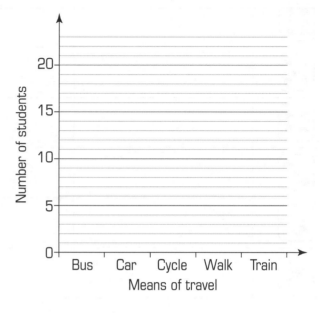

2 Chloe recorded the temperature every hour, for 8 hours.

a Plot her data as a line graph on the grid. The graph has been started for you.

Time	Temperature
10.00	9 °C
11.00	12 °C
12.00	14 °C
13.00	16 °C
14.00	19 °C
15.00	13 °C
16.00	14 °C
17.00	11 °C

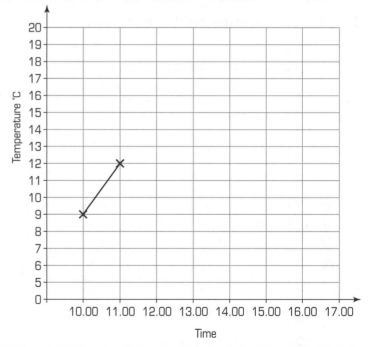

b When was the highest temperature recorded? _____

c Was the temperature increasing or decreasing between 11.00 and 12.00? _____

I can do
this page!

1 Here are some friends' results in a Maths test:

| 3 | 5 | 7 | 8 | 10 | 12 | 12 |
| 13 | 14 | 15 | 18 | 19 | 20 | 20 |

a Group the data into classes by completing this table:

Scores	1 2 3 4 5	6 7 8 9 10	11 12 13 14 15	16 17 18 19 20
Grouped scores	1–5	6–10	11–15	16–20
Tally	II			
Number of students	2			

b Complete the bar chart for the data on this grid:

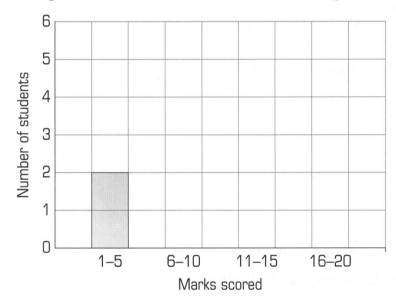

2 Here are the friends' Science results:

| 2 | 3 | 5 | 6 | 7 | 7 | 10 |
| 12 | 14 | 16 | 17 | 18 | 18 | 19 |

What is **a** the lowest result? _____ **b** the highest result? _____

c Group the data into classes in this table:

Grouped scores	1–5	6–10	11–15	16–20
Number of students				

1 This pattern of tiles is in the ratio 1 : 3 (black : white).

Draw patterns with these ratios in the boxes.

a | 1 : 4 (black : white)

b | 3 : 1 (black : white)

2 Here is a pattern of blue and white beads:

a What is the ratio of blue : white beads? _____

b Use this space to make a pattern with 4 blue beads in the same ratio.

3 Colour the correct number of tins of blue paint for the second mix, so that both mixes are the same shade of blue.

First mix **1 : 4**

Second mix

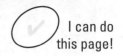

1 Here is a recipe for bread and butter pudding.

It makes enough for 4 people.

| 8 slices of bread |
| 2 eggs |
| 200 ml milk |
| 50 g sugar |
| 250 g sultanas |

a Complete this table.

Some parts have been done to help you.

	bread (slices)	eggs	milk (ml)	sugar (g)	sultanas (g)
4 people	8	2			
2 people					125

b Complete this table for the recipe for 6 people.

	bread (slices)	eggs	milk (ml)	sugar (g)	sultanas (g)
6 people					

2 Concrete is made from cement, sand, gravel and water.

This mixture makes enough concrete for one quarter $\left(\frac{1}{4}\right)$ of a shed floor.

Cement	30 kg
Sand	90 kg
Gravel	20 kg
Water	7 litres

Complete the table to work out the mixture to concrete the whole floor.

	cement (kg)	sand (kg)	gravel (kg)	water (litres)
$\frac{1}{4}$ of the floor	30	90		
whole floor				

Maths life

The sandwich bar

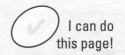

Choose one main filling ... + **... add one extra**

chicken   beef   ham
egg   cheese   tuna
chilli   baked beans

pickle   mustard
mayonnaise   lettuce
cucumber   tomato
sweetcorn   onion

add a second main filling for only 50p

add more extras for only 15p each

baguette £2.20

roll £1.40

sandwich £1.60

baked potato £2.25

1. Find the total cost of these three orders:

ORDER A

4 cheese and onion baked potatoes

total cost = ...

ORDER B

1 beef and mustard baguette

1 ham and pickle baguette

2 egg and mayonnaise sandwiches

total cost = ...

ORDER C

1 chicken and pickle roll

1 egg, cucumber and tomato roll

1 ham and cheese sandwich

total cost = ...

2. How much change would you get from £10 for each of the orders?

Order A:
....

Order B:
....

Order C:
....

Make up your own order.
Don't spend more than £10.
What change do you get from £10?
Can you spend exactly £10?

ORDER:

TOTAL COST = ...

▶ The perimeter of a shape is the total distance around the edge.

Fill in the calculation to find the perimeter of each shape.

1

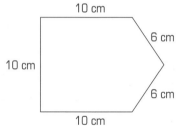

8 cm

5 cm   5 cm

8 cm

The perimeter of this rectangle $= 8 + 5 + 8 + 5$ cm

$= 8 + 8 + 5 + 5$ cm

$= 2 \times \underline{\hspace{1cm}}$ cm $+ 2 \times \underline{\hspace{1cm}}$ cm

$= \underline{\hspace{1cm}}$ cm

2

10 cm

6 cm

10 cm

6 cm

10 cm

Perimeter $= \underline{\hspace{0.7cm}}$ cm $+ \underline{\hspace{0.7cm}}$ cm $+ \underline{\hspace{0.7cm}}$ cm $+ \underline{\hspace{0.7cm}}$ cm $+ \underline{\hspace{0.7cm}}$ cm

$= 3 \times \underline{\hspace{1cm}}$ cm $+ 2 \times \underline{\hspace{1cm}}$ cm

3

$= \underline{\hspace{2cm}}$ cm

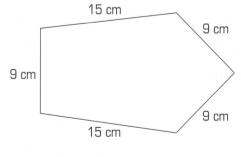

15 cm

9 cm

9 cm

9 cm

15 cm

9 cm

$= \underline{\hspace{0.7cm}}$ cm $+ \underline{\hspace{0.7cm}}$ cm $+ \underline{\hspace{0.7cm}}$ cm $+ \underline{\hspace{0.7cm}}$ cm $+ \underline{\hspace{0.7cm}}$ cm

$= \underline{\hspace{0.7cm}} \times \underline{\hspace{0.7cm}}$ cm $+ \underline{\hspace{0.7cm}} \times \underline{\hspace{0.7cm}}$ cm

$= \underline{\hspace{2cm}}$ cm

When you draw **one line** across a box you make 2 spaces (marked 1 and 2).

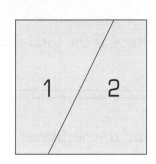

You can write it as:

lines: 1

spaces: 2

Count the lines and spaces in these 4 diagrams.

1

lines: _____

spaces: _____

2

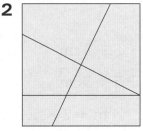

lines: _____

spaces: _____

3

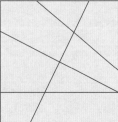

lines: _____

spaces: _____

4

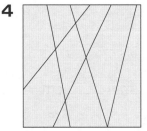

lines: _____

spaces: _____

5 Complete this sentence about the numbers of lines and spaces.

The number of spaces is _____ the number of lines.

6 Write the formula that links the number of lines and

the number of spaces.

Start: number of spaces = _____

or s = _____

13c Two operations

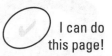

1 Fill in the outputs of these machines.

a
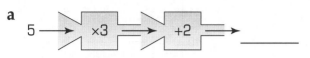

b
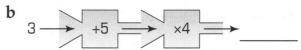

c
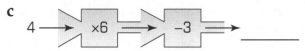

d
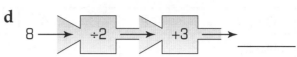

2 Complete the machines to work out the value of the symbol.

a
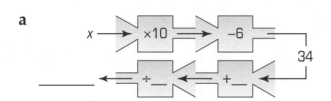

b
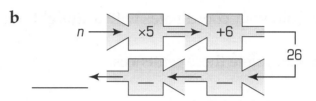

3 In this dice game, James's score is 5 when he lands on the

first question mark.

He rolls 4 to land on the second question mark.

Now his score is 27.

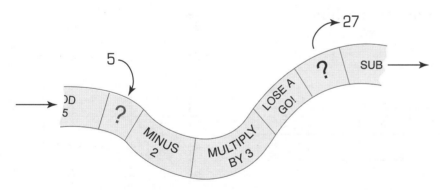

Which two operations must be covered by the question marks?

Pick from the box and write them on the machines.

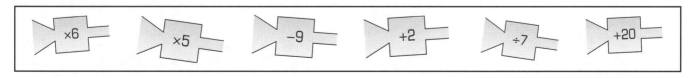

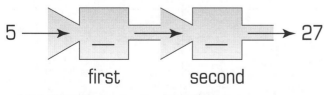

first   second

1 a Complete the table for this function machine:

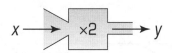

input, x	1	2	3	4	5	6
output, y	2					

b Plot the coordinates onto this grid.

c Join your coordinates with a straight line.

d Complete these sentences:

The y-coordinate is _____

the x-coordinate.

The function is $y =$ _____ x.

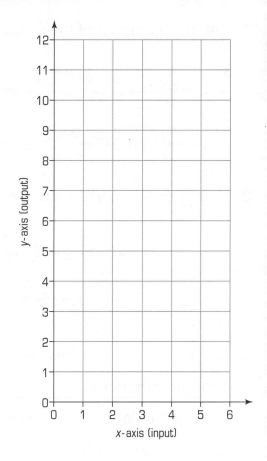

y-axis (output)

x-axis (input)

2 a Complete the table for this function machine:

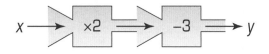

input, x	0	1	2	3	4	5
output, y	-3	-1				

b Plot the coordinates onto this grid.

c Join them with a straight line.

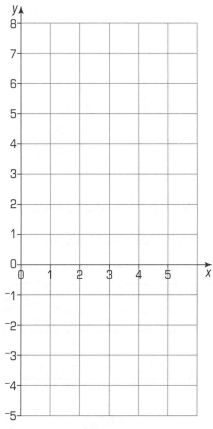

13f Horizontal and vertical lines

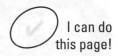

I can do this page!

1 Plot these sets of points on the grid.

Join each set with a straight line.

a Line A: (1, 1) (5, 1) (8, 1)

b Line B: (1, 2) (1, 4) (1, 8)

c Line C: (7, 1) (7, 5) (7, 8)

All of the y-coordinates in line A are 1.

You can write line A as $y = 1$.

Complete these sentences for the other lines:

d Line B is called $x =$ _____

e Line C is called $x =$ _____

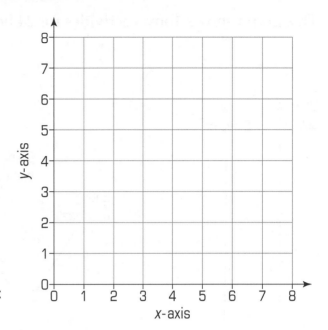

2 For each line:

▶ Choose 3 coordinates

▶ Plot them

▶ Join them to make a line.

a Line A: $y = 3$

(____, 3) (____, 3) (____, 3)

b Line B: $x = 5$

(5, ____) (5, ____) (5, ____)

c Line C: $y = 1$

(____, 1) (____, ____) (____, ____)

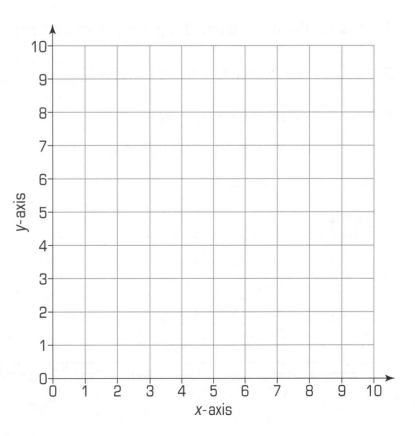

55

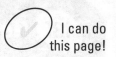

This graph shows Tony's activities for 24 hours on a Saturday.

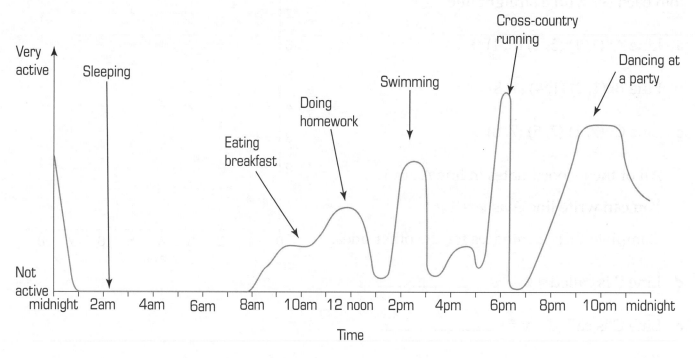

1 What is the most active thing Tony does on Saturday? _____

2 What is the least active thing he does? _____

3 Draw your own activity graph.

Say what day of the week your graph shows.

Day: _____

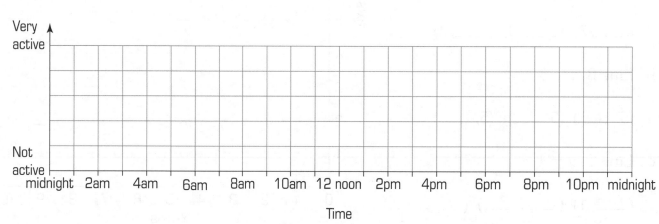

14a Measuring lines

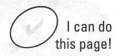

1   Measure the dimensions of the model cottage, and record the measurements to the nearest millimetre.

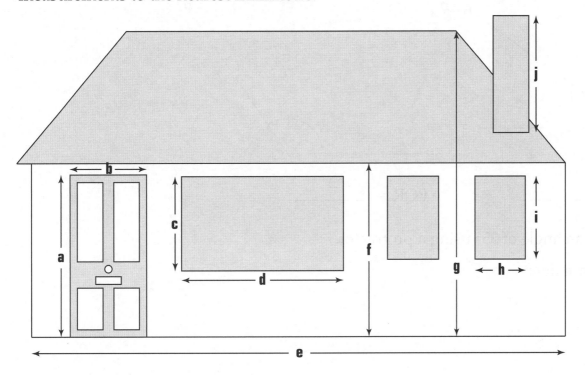

a   The door is _____ cm high.

b   The door is _____ cm wide.

c   The big window is _____ cm high.

d   The big window is _____ cm wide.

e   The cottage is _____ cm wide.

f   The front of the cottage is _____ cm high.

g   The total height of the cottage is _____ cm.

h   The small window is _____ cm wide.

i   The small window is _____ cm high.

j   The chimney is _____ cm high.

> Your answer will be a decimal, for example, 3.1 cm

1   Measure these two angles with a protractor.

a 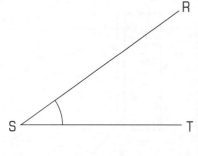   b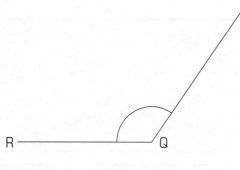

RST = _____ °   PQR = _____ °

2   Construct an angle of 35° using a protractor.

Use this base line:

3   Use a protractor, pencil and ruler to construct these triangles.

The base line is drawn for you, and the size of each angle is given.

a   b

50°   30°   70°   45°

14d Area of rectangular shapes

✓ I can do this page!

This is a plan of the Oxford Square Youth Club.

The measurements of each room are in metres.

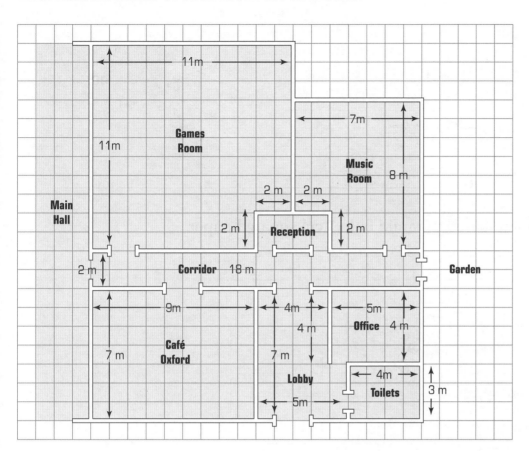

1 Find the area of:

a   The Office _____ m²   b   The Corridor _____ m²

c   Café Oxford _____ m²   d   The Lobby _____ m²

e   The Music Room _____ m²   f   The Games Room _____ m²

2 Floorshow Ltd clean the floors of the Youth Club.

They charge 30 pence for each **square metre** of floor.

How much does it cost to clean:

a   The Toilets _____ p

b   The Games Room _____ p

c   Café Oxford? _____ p

1 Using a ruler, join the dots in order to make a solid shape.

Name each shape.

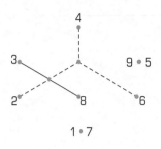 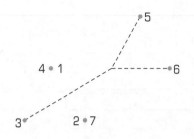 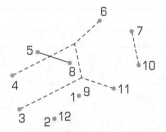

a _____ b _____ c _____

2 Copy this net for a square-based pyramid onto 1 cm squared paper.

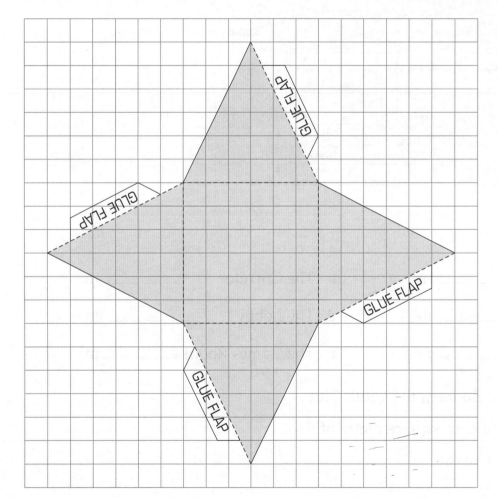

▶ Cut out the shape.

▶ Fold along the dotted lines.

▶ Glue the edges together using the flaps.

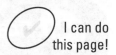
This box is an open cube.

It has no lid.

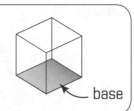
base

1 Each of these nets folds to make an open cube.

Colour the square that will be the base of the cube.

a

b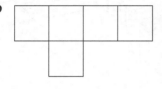

c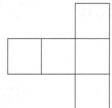

d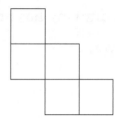

e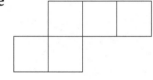

f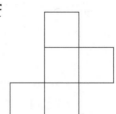

g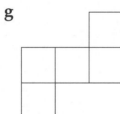

h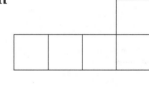

2 Each of these nets folds to make a different shape.

Draw lines to connect each shape to its net.

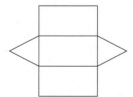

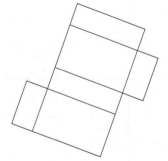

14g Scale drawings

Draw the view of the house and garden from above.

Use the grid below.

Use the scale 1 cm : 1 m.

1 cm represents 1 m.

The drawing has been started for you.

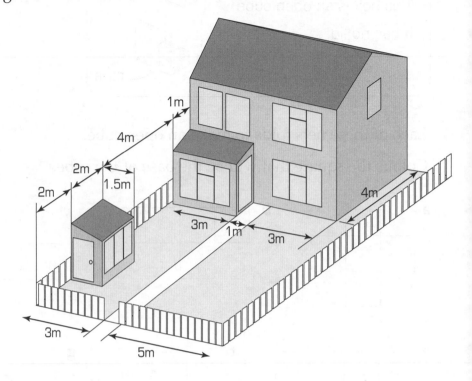

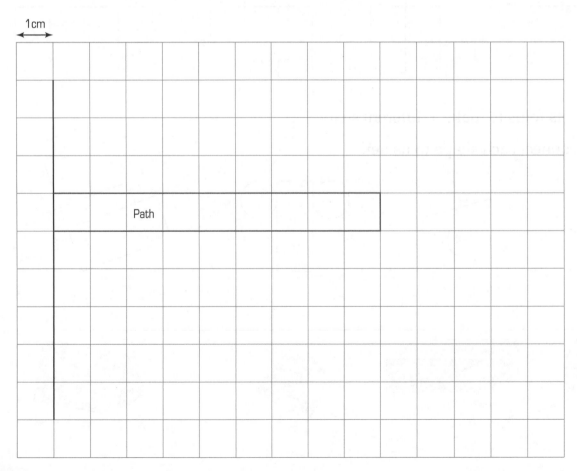

1cm

Path

1 Level out these piles of cakes to make equal height piles.

What is the new height of each pile?

a

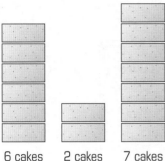

6 cakes   2 cakes   7 cakes

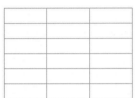

Height = _____

b

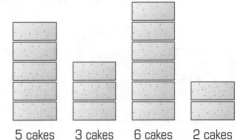

5 cakes   3 cakes   6 cakes   2 cakes

Height = _____

2 Ricky throws 3 darts. He scores 21 with the first dart,

13 with the second and 11 with the third dart.

a What is Ricky's total score?   _____

b What is his **mean** score?   _____

3 Pete works in the market each evening after school.

He earned these amounts over 5 evenings:

£6   £13   £7   £5   £9

$$\text{Mean} = \frac{\text{total of values}}{\text{number of values}}$$

a What are his **total** earnings?   _____

b What is the **mean** of his earnings?   _____

4 Over 1 term Karen got these marks in her Science assessments:

14   12   18   16

a What is the **total** of her marks?   _____

b What is the **mean** of her marks?   _____

Students in 8W make model gliders in Technology.

They fly their gliders to see which is the most successful design.

Each student has 3 trials. Here are their results to the nearest metre:

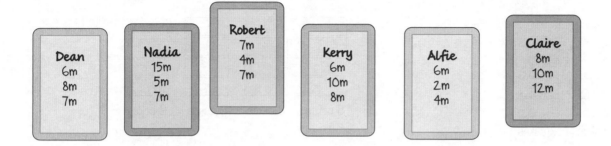

Dean
6m
8m
7m

Nadia
15m
5m
7m

Robert
7m
4m
7m

Kerry
6m
10m
8m

Alfie
6m
2m
4m

Claire
8m
10m
12m

1 a What distance was the longest flight? _____

b What distance was the shortest flight? _____

c What is the range of distances? _____

2 a Write this data on this data collection sheet.

Name	Trial			Total	Mean
	1	2	3		
Dean					
Nadia					
Robert					
Kerry					
Alfie					
Claire					

b Total the distances and fill in the total column.

c Divide the total by 3 to fill in the **mean** distance for each student.

3 Whose glider did the best? Explain your answer.

_____

_____

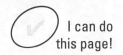
These students have all written a report, but have each made errors.

1 Shaun says:

*Size 11 is the **mode** because size 11 is the biggest shoe size in the survey.*

What is wrong with Shaun's statement?

Shoe Size	Tally	Frequency
7	⽶ ⽶ ⽶ III	18
8	⽶ ⽶ ⽶ ⽶ ⽶ ⽶ II	32
9	⽶ ⽶ ⽶ ⽶ III	23
10	⽶ III	8
11	III	3

_____

_____

_____

2 Lara produces a bar chart.

What errors can you spot?

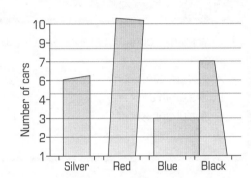

_____

_____

_____

_____

3 Kenny's report begins:

My investigation is about how young people spend their leisure time. I interviewed my 3 best friends, and used this data to make a pie chart.

What is wrong with Kenny's investigation?

_____

_____

4 Kelly's hypothesis is *'Younger people go to the cinema more often than older people.'*

What **important** question is missing from her data collection sheet?

Name	Male/ Female	How many times did you go to the cinema this year?	What film did you last see?

_____

_____

Maths life

Recycling and energy

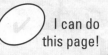

Each aluminium drink can that is recycled saves enough energy to run a television set for three hours.

3 hours

1 How many hours of television would you power by recycling:
   a 2 aluminium cans
   b 3 aluminium cans
   c 4 aluminium cans
   d 10 aluminium cans?

2 How many cans would save enough energy for:
   a 6 hours of TV
   b 12 hours of TV
   c 15 hours of TV
   d 24 hours of TV?

Making 1 new aluminium can uses the same amount of energy as recycling 20 cans.

3 How many recycled cans could you make using the same amount of energy as:
   a 2 new cans
   b 5 new cans?

Roughly how many cans do you drink in a week? How many hours of television could you power by recycling those cans?

Checklist – I can do it!

Multiplication table

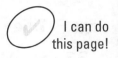

×	1	2	3	4	5	6	7	8	9	10	11	12
1	1	2	3	4	5	6	7	8	9	10	11	12
2	2	4	6	8	10	12	14	16	18	20	22	24
3	3	6	9	12	15	18	21	24	27	30	33	36
4	4	8	12	16	20	24	28	32	36	40	44	48
5	5	10	15	20	25	30	35	40	45	50	55	60
6	6	12	18	24	30	36	42	48	54	60	66	72
7	7	14	21	28	35	42	49	56	63	70	77	84
8	8	16	24	32	40	48	56	64	72	80	88	96
9	9	18	27	36	45	54	63	72	81	90	99	108
10	10	20	30	40	50	60	70	80	90	100	110	120
11	11	22	33	44	55	66	77	88	99	110	121	132
12	12	24	36	48	60	72	84	96	108	120	132	144